The Best Of

enya

ISBN 1-85909-385-X

IMP **International Music Publications Limited**
Southend Road, Woodford Green, Essex IG8 8HN, England

AFER VENTUS

Written by ROMA RYAN
Composed and Arranged by
ENYA and NICKY RYAN

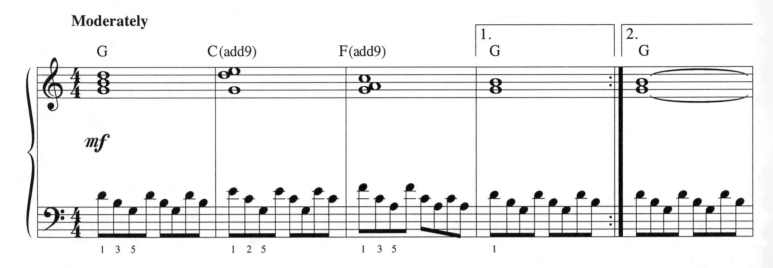

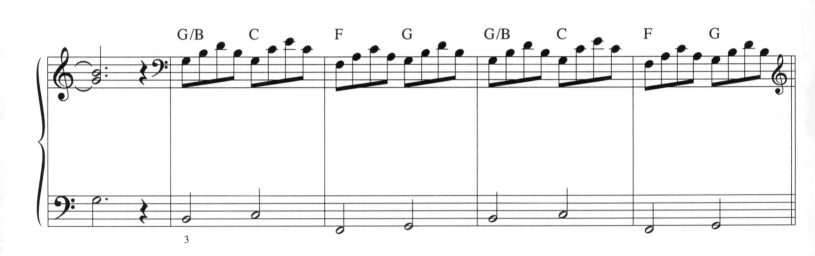

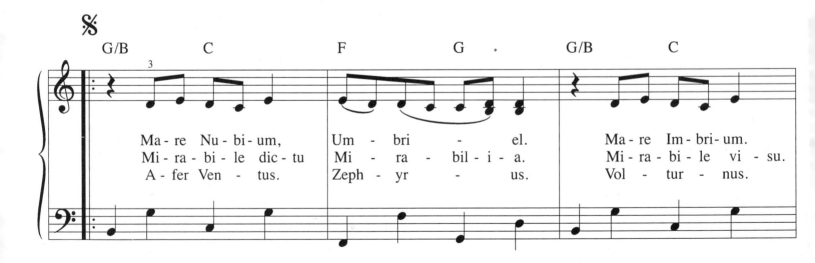

Mare Nu - bi - um,   Um - bri - el.   Mare Im - bri - um.
Mi - ra - bi - le dic - tu   Mi - ra - bil - i - a.   Mi - ra - bi - le vi - su.
A - fer Ven - tus.   Zeph - yr - us.   Vol - tur - nus.

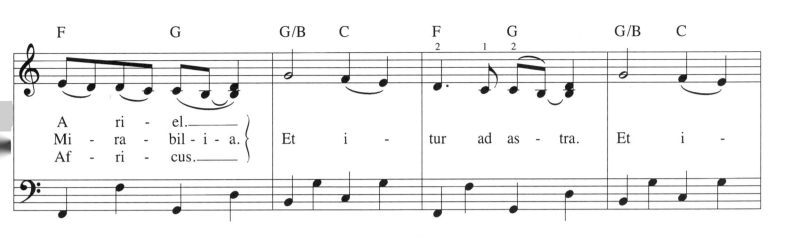

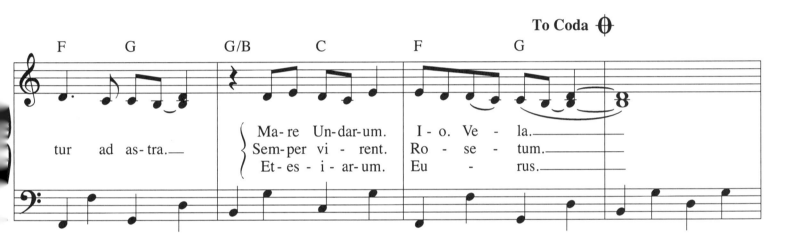

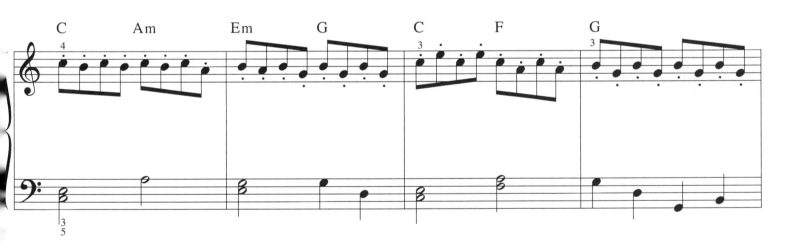

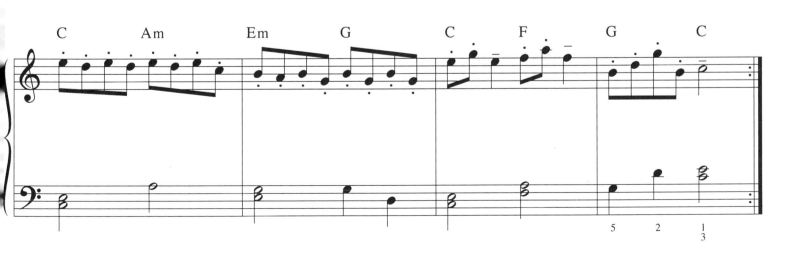

4

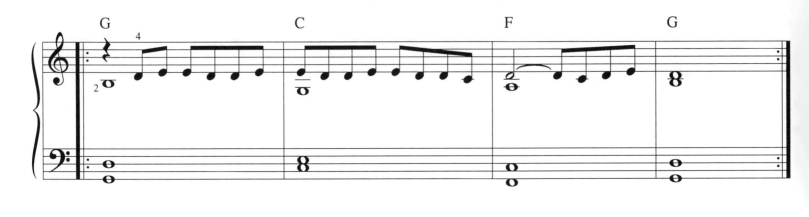

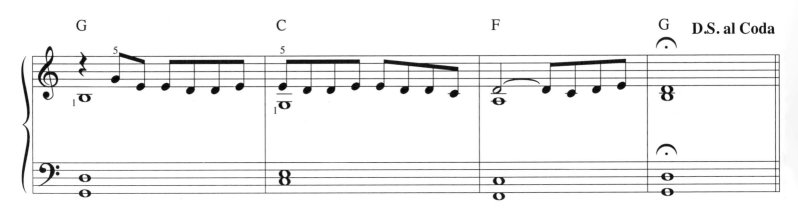

CODA

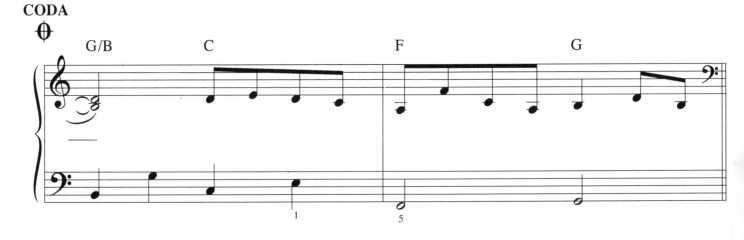

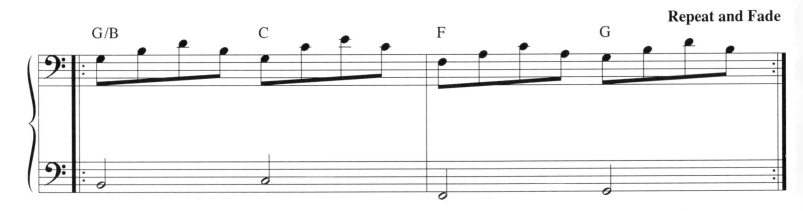

Running verse:

Suus cuique mos. Suum cuique.
Meus mihi, suus cuique carus.
Memento, terrigena.
Memento, vita brevis.
Meus mihi, suus cuique carus.

NO HOLLY FOR MISS QUINN

Composed and Arranged by
ENYA and NICKY RYAN

Slow and free

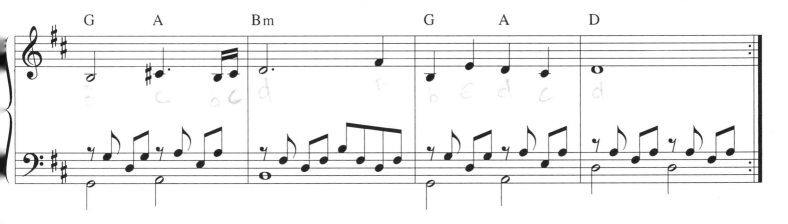

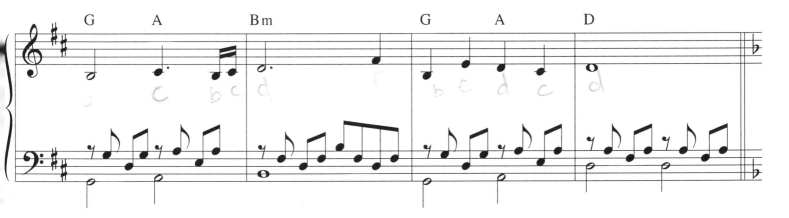

BOOK OF DAYS

Composed and Arranged by
ENYA and NICKY RYAN

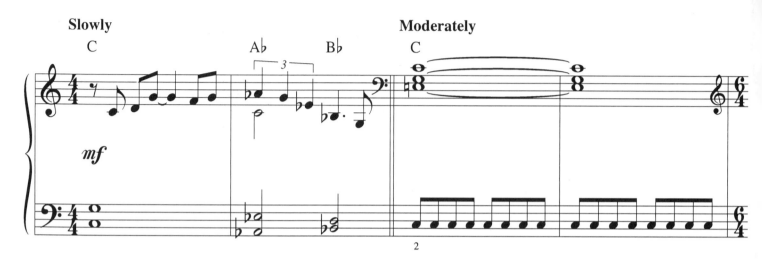

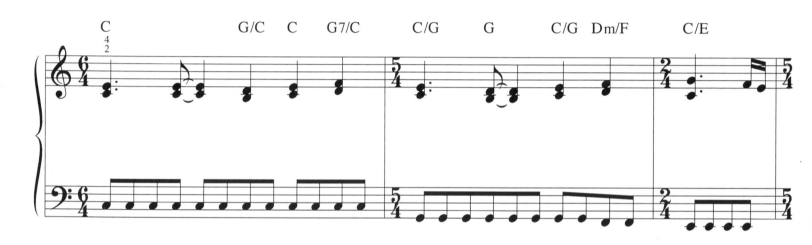

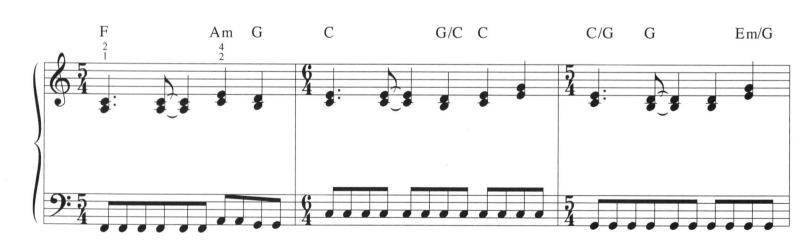

Ó oiche go hoích, mo thuras,
An bealach fada romhan.
Ó lá go lá, mo thuras,
na scéalta na mbeidh a choich.

CARIBBEAN BLUE

Composed and Arranged by
ENYA and NICKY RYAN

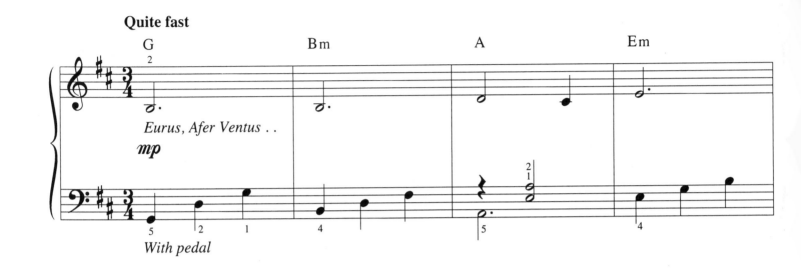

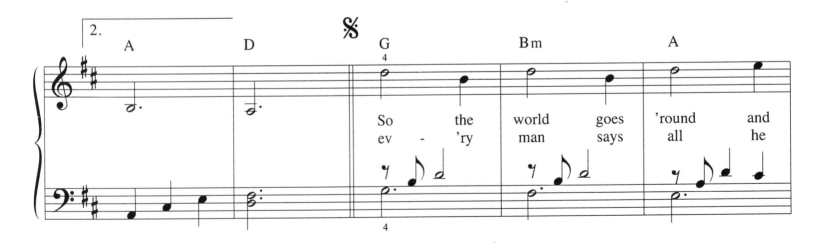

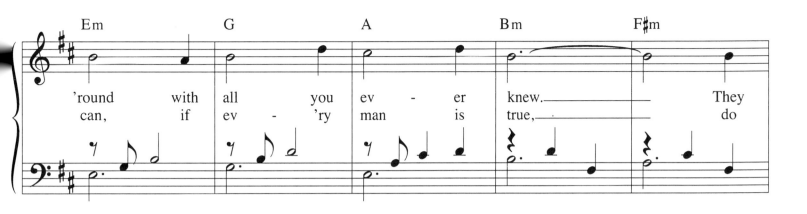

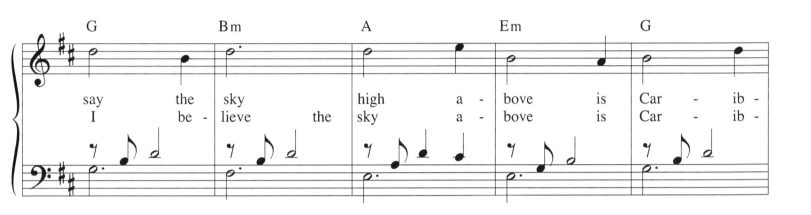

14

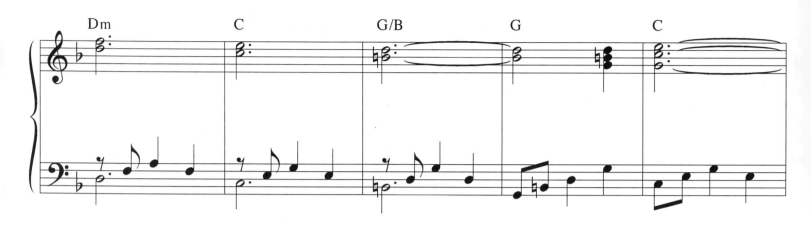

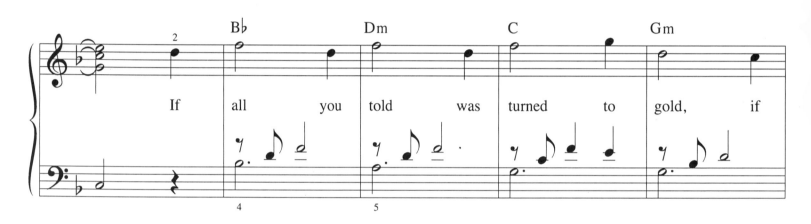

If all you told was turned to gold, if

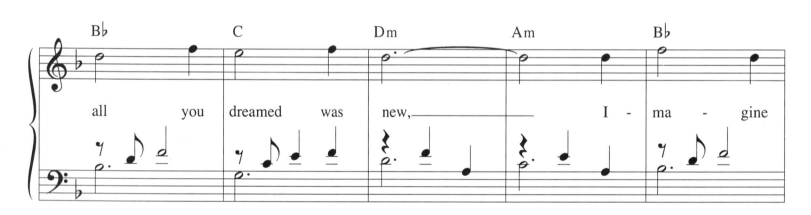

all you dreamed was new,_____ I - ma - gine

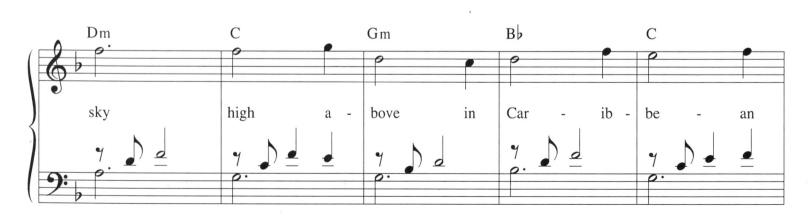

sky high a - bove in Car - ib - be - an

blue.

Eurus, Afer Ventus, Boreas Zephyrus, Africus . . .

THE CELTS

Written and Composed by ENYA,
NICKY RYAN and ROMA RYAN

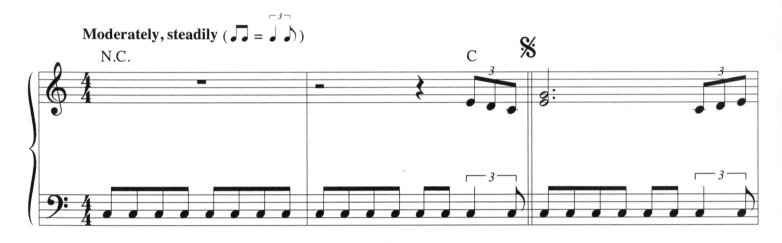

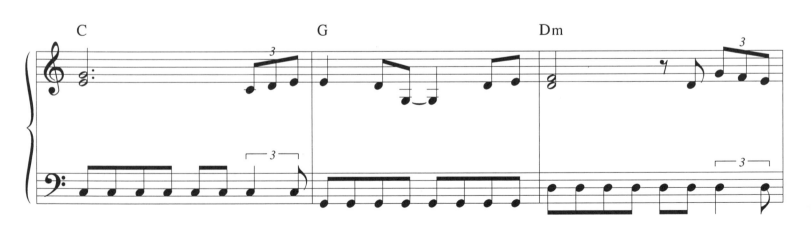

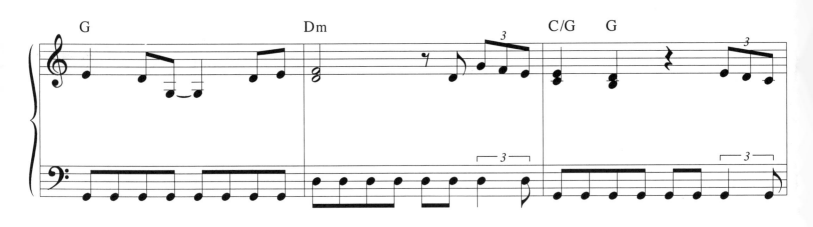

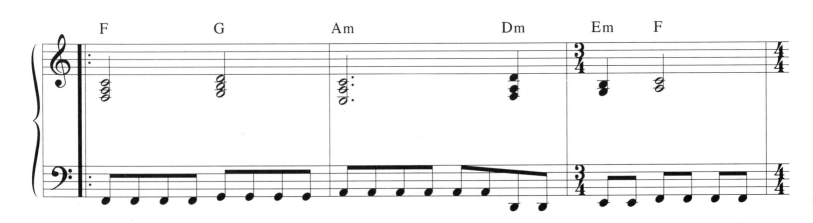

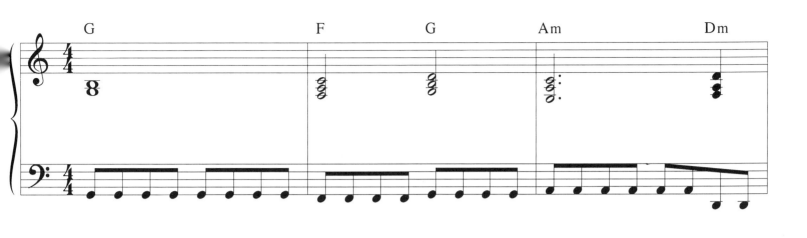

D.S. al Coda

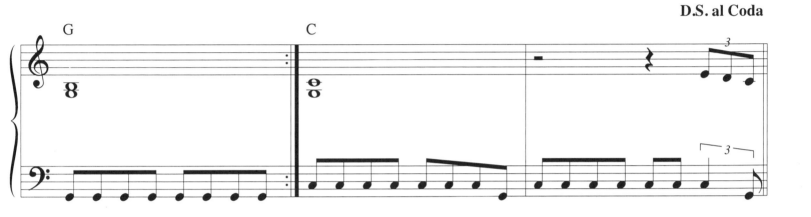

CODA

FAIRYTALE

Written and Composed by ENYA,
NICKY RYAN and ROMA RYAN

sempre staccato, lightly

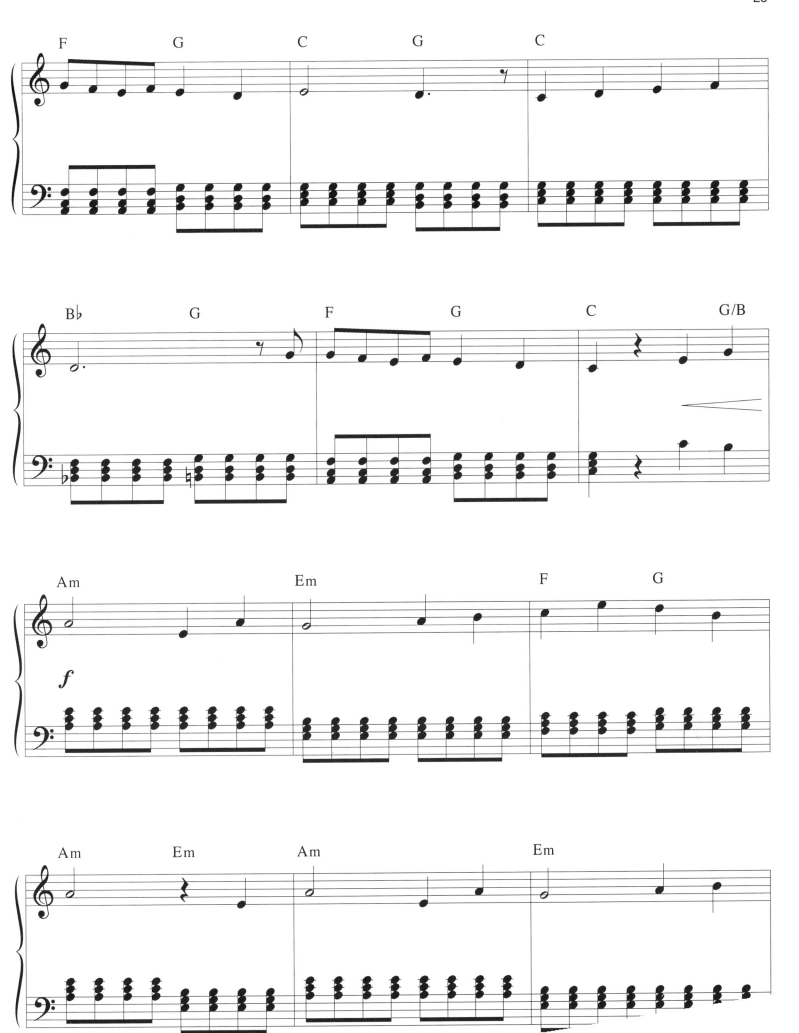

ORINOCO FLOW

Music by ENYA
Words by ROMA RYAN

Play cue note on repeat and D.S. only.

28

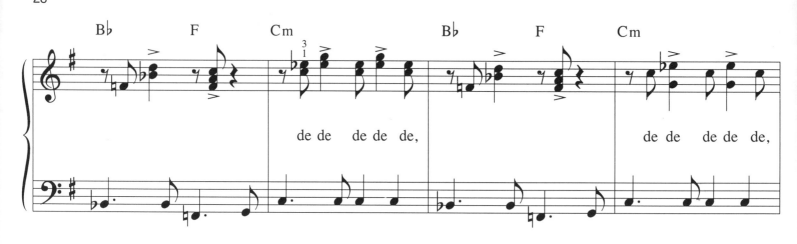

de de de de de,   de de de de de,

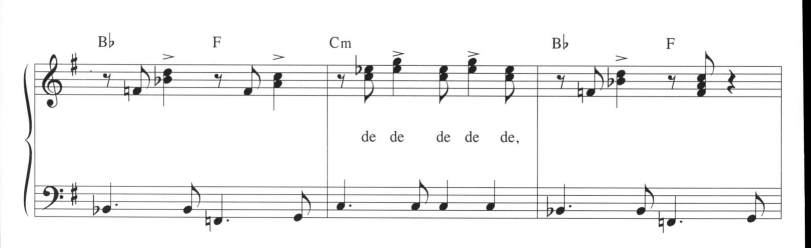

de de de de de,

de de de de de.   Sail a - way, sail a-way, sail a-

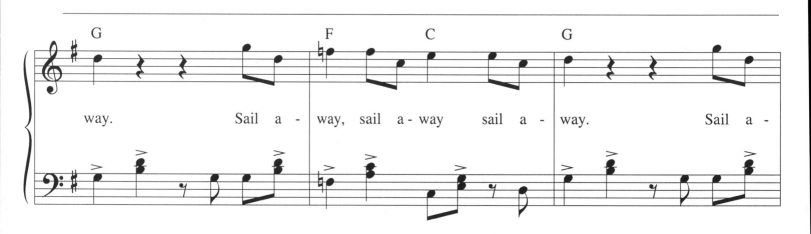

way.   Sail a - way, sail a-way sail a - way.   Sail a-

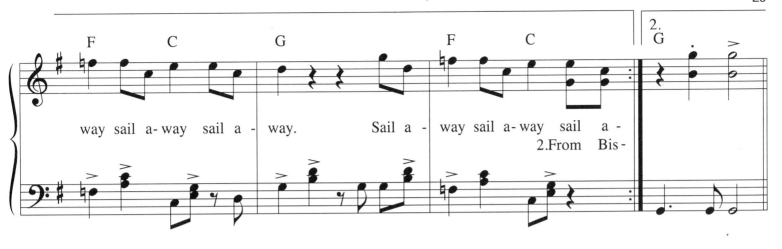

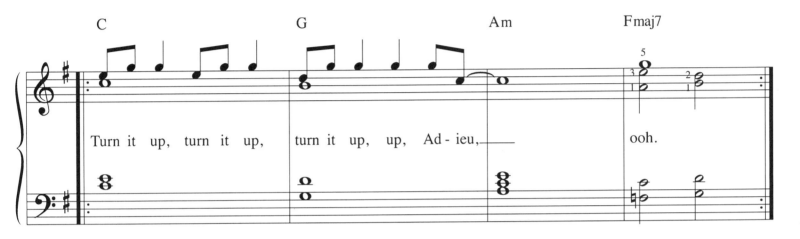

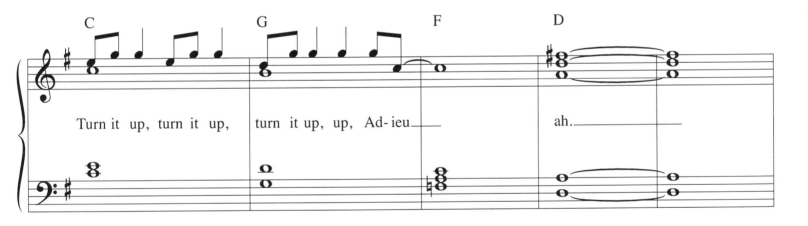

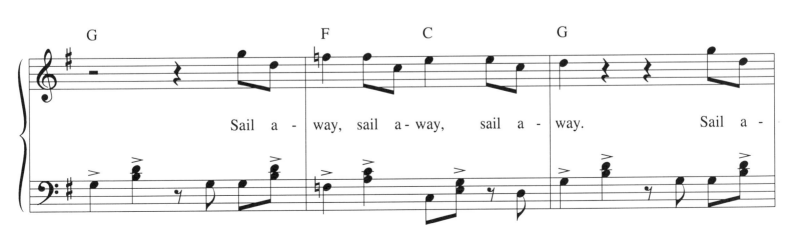

31

Dick-ins at the wheel,— we can sigh,— say good-bye— Ross and his de-pen-den-cies. We can

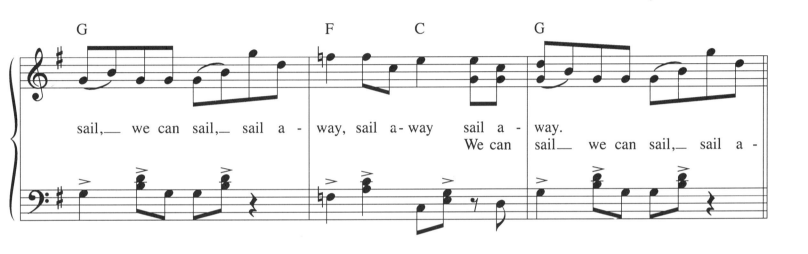

sail,— we can sail,— sail a - way, sail a-way sail a - way.
We can sail— we can sail,— sail a-

Repeat and Fade

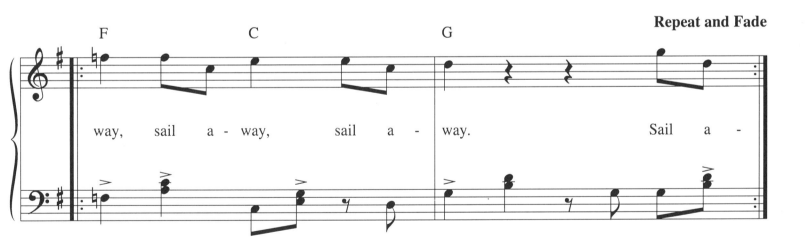

way, sail a - way, sail a - way. Sail a -

Additional Lyrics

From Bissau to Palau in the shade of Avalon
From Fiji to Tiree and the Isles of Ebony
From Peru to Cebu, feel the power of Babylon
From Bali to Cali far beneath the Coral Sea.

From the North to the South, Ebadae unto Khartoum
From the deep Sea of Clouds to the Island of the Moon
Carry me on the waves to the lands I've never been
Carry me on the waves to the lands I've never seen.

ON YOUR SHORE

Music by ENYA
Words by NICKY RYAN

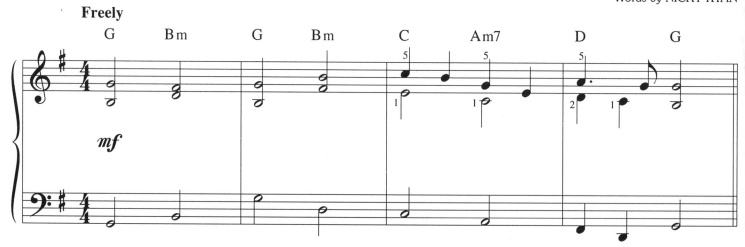

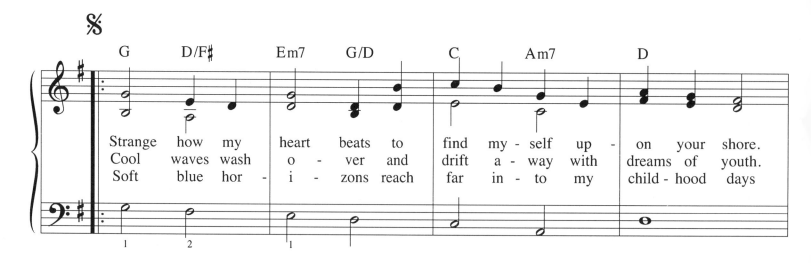

Strange how my heart beats to find my-self up - on your shore.
Cool waves wash o - ver and drift a - way with dreams of youth.
Soft blue hor - i - zons reach far in - to my child - hood days

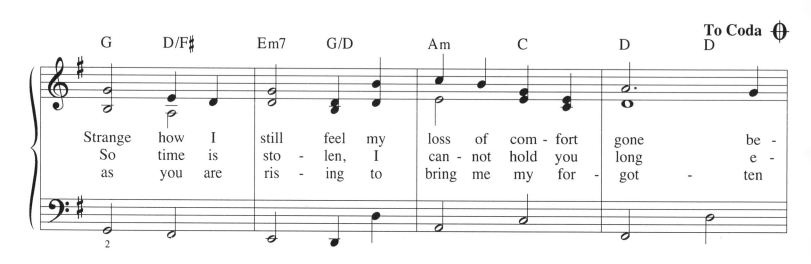

Strange how I still feel my loss of com - fort gone be -
So time is sto - len, I can - not hold you long e -
as you are ris - ing to bring me my for - got - ten

D.S. al Coda

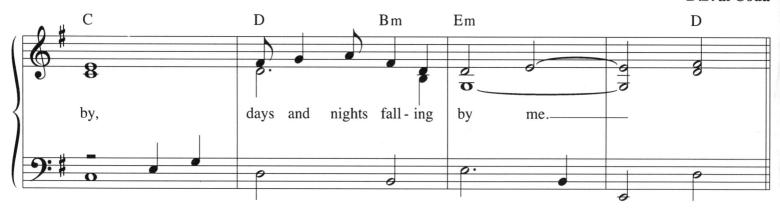

by, days and nights fall-ing by me.

CODA

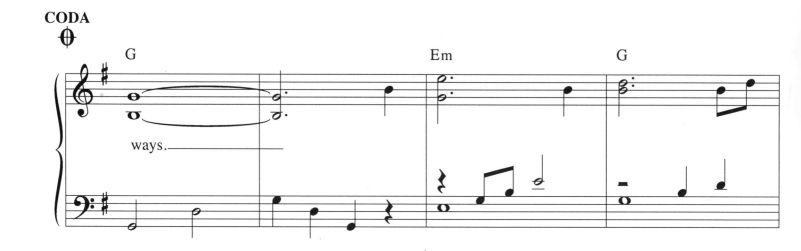

ways.

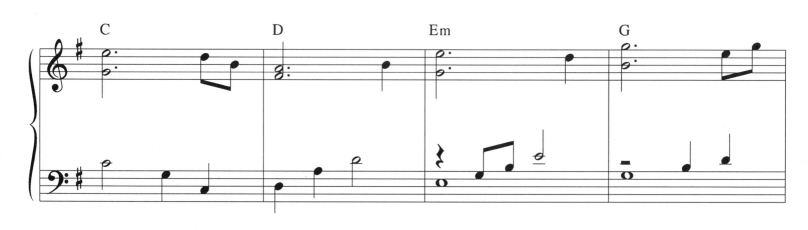

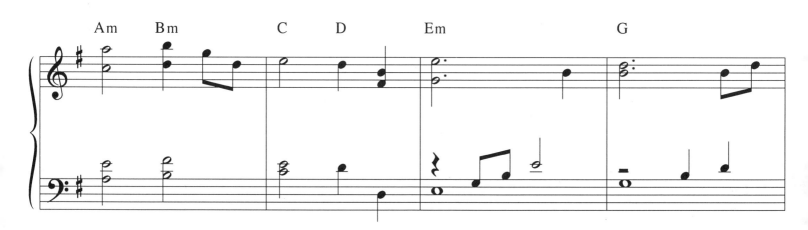

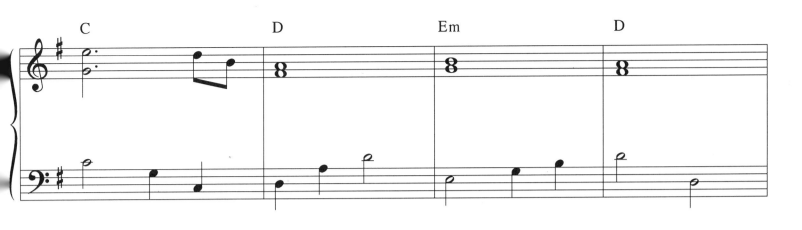

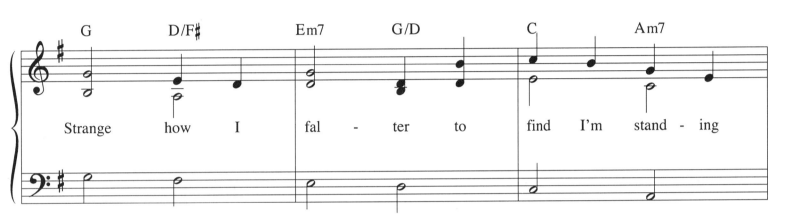

Strange how I fal - ter to find I'm stand - ing

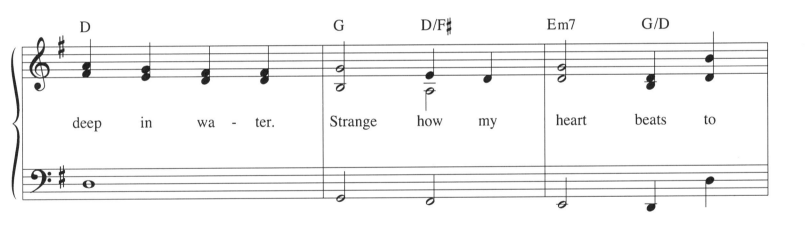

deep in wa - ter. Strange how my heart beats to

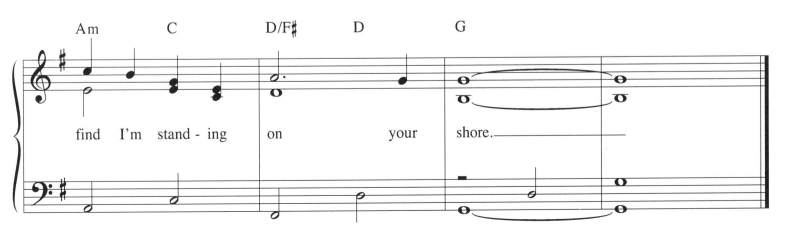

find I'm stand - ing on your shore.

SHEPHERD MOONS

Composed and Arranged by
ENYA and NICKY RYAN

STORMS IN AFRICA

Music by ENYA
Words by ROMA RYAN

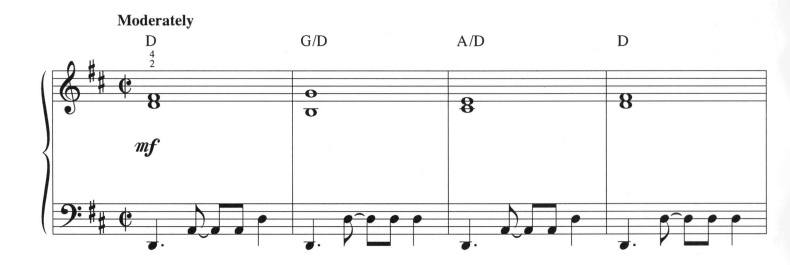

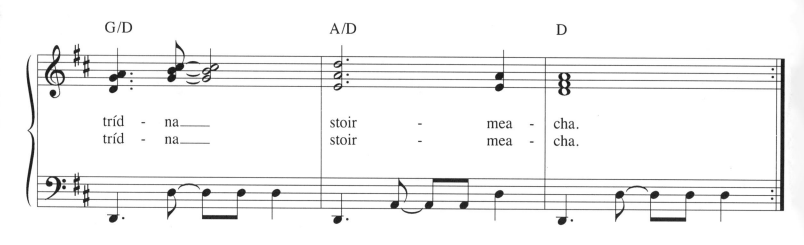

41

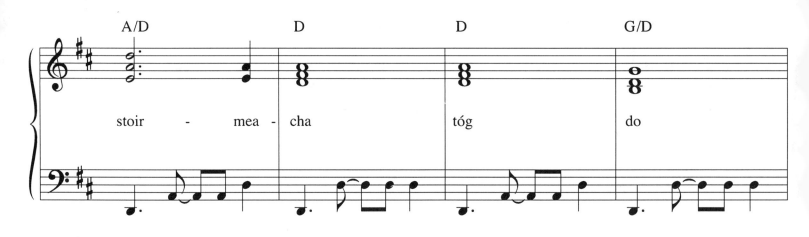

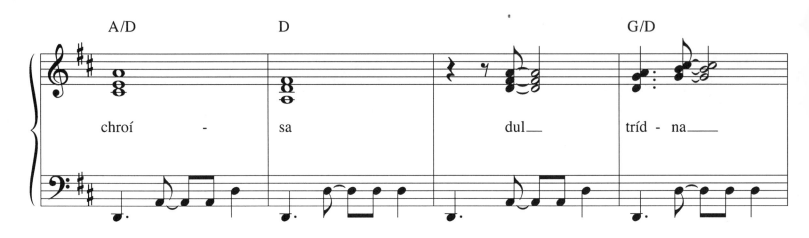

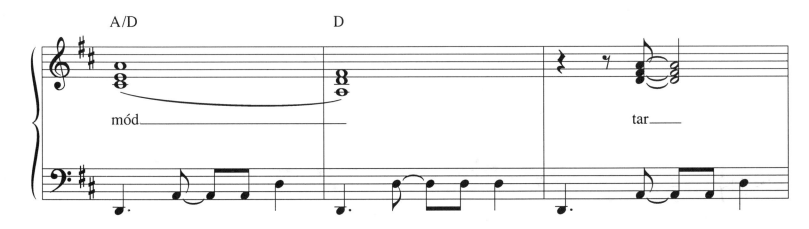

tríd - na____ stoir - mea - cha. Tur -

as____ fa - da an___ harc

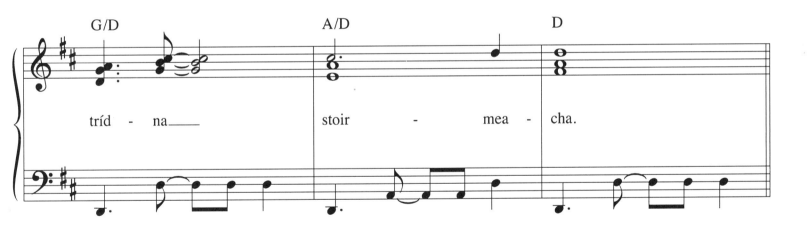

tríd - na____ stoir - mea - cha.

Repeat and Fade

TO GO BEYOND

Written and Composed by ENYA,
NICKY RYAN and ROMA RYAN

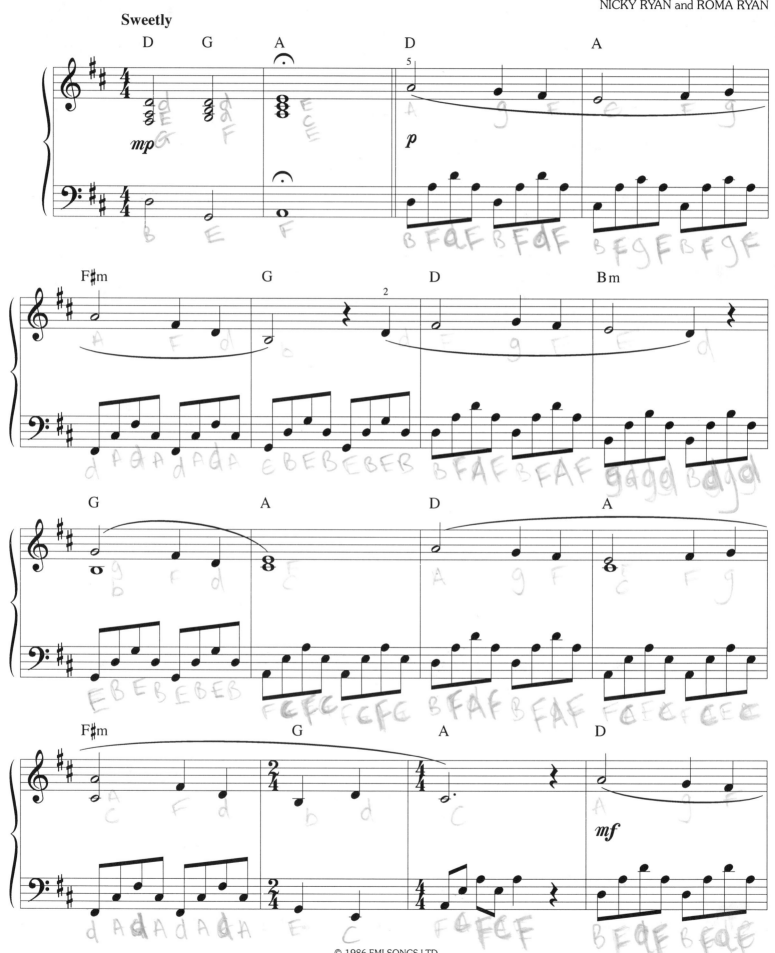

WATERMARK

Music by ENYA
Words by ROMA RYAN

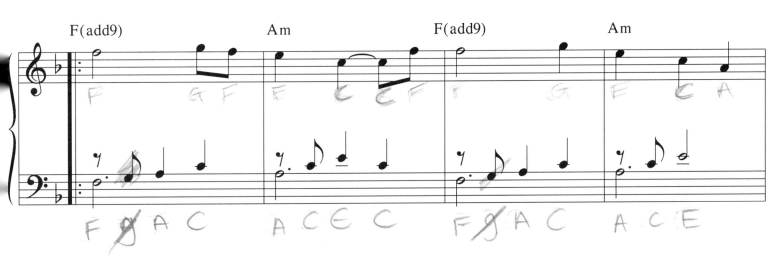

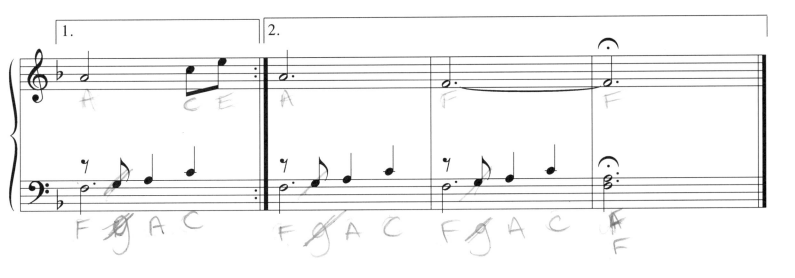

R -

L - F C g A g C F X3

C#

D
C#
A#
C#
F A#
F

C g A g D C g

F X1
A X1
F X1
A X1
B#
E #
F X3
C C F C
F F F

L - F C g A g C F X3

A E A C A E A X1

F X1

A X1

B# F B# c d

E# B# E# f g

F X3   A X1

A X1   B#

F X1   E#

F X2   A X1
∩   D X1
D A D E F   A X1
                E X1
A X1
E #